STEM *Activit*

CW00530758

AMAZING
MATHS

THIS IS A CARLTON BOOK

Text, design and illustration
© Carlton Books Limited 2018

Published in 2018 by Carlton Books Limited
An imprint of the Carlton Publishing Group
20 Mortimer Street, London W1T 3JW

A catalogue record for this book is available from the British Library.

ISBN: 978-1-78312-361-2

Printed in China
10 9 8 7 6 5 4 3 2 1

Executive editor: Bryony Davies
Editors: Selina Wood and Sonya Newland
Design: Kate Wiliwinska
Designed and illustrated by: Dynamo Limited
Picture research: Steve Behan and Paul Langan
Production: Nicola Davey

AUTHOR:

HANNAH WILSON has edited and written children's non-fiction for 20 years. With a particular interest in STEM, she has made more than 100 titles – books about astronauts and space, the human body, technology and the natural world, as well as revision guides and science-based reading schemes. She has written many titles about animals, including Carlton's 'iExplore Bugs', which won a best-book award at the Bologna Book Fair 2018 (Ragazzi Digital Award).

STEM EDITORIAL CONSULTANT:

MARGARET (MEG) KÄUFER is a founding member and current President of the STEM Alliance of Larchmont-Mamaroneck, NY. The STEM Alliance is a non-profit organisation with the mission of creating a network of STEM learning opportunities to connect today's youth to the jobs of the future. They work closely with local schools to run hands-on, applied STEM enrichment experiences. Highlights of their work under her leadership include launching an annual public STEM festival, establishing competitive robotics teams, and creating a hands-on STEM summer enrichment program for at-risk children. Meg has her Masters in Curriculum & Instruction from Teachers College — Columbia University. Throughout her career, Meg has championed STEM learning for its capacity to engage and inspire all varieties of learners.

PICTURE ACKNOWLEDGEMENTS

The publishers would like to thank the following sources for their kind permission to reproduce the pictures in the book.

Pages 6-7: Alexandr III/Shutterstock; 10-11 (background): Aklionka/Shutterstock; 12 (top right): Public Domain; 13 (right): MicroOne/Shutterstock; 14-15 (background): Inspiring/Shutterstock; 14 (bottom left): Kirill Kirsanov/Shutterstock; 16 (hamster): Kuttelvaserova Stuchelova/Shutterstock, (cat): Peter Wollinga/Shutterstock, (dog): Cynoclub/Shutterstock; 18-19 (background): Kelvin Degree/Shutterstock; 19 (bottom left): Studio_G/Shutterstock; 23 (centre): VectorPixelStar/Shutterstock, (bottom): Mary Terriberry/Shutterstock; 24 (bottom right): Attaphong/Shutterstock; 29 (left): 89studio/Shutterstock, (right): Lekkystockphoto/Shutterstock; 30 (smart phone): Stanisic Vladimir/Shutterstock; 32-33 (clock face): Attaphong/Shutterstock; 34 (top right): Harlowbutler/Shutterstock; 40-41 (butterflies): Butterfly Hunter/Shutterstock; 41 (notebook): 89studio/Shutterstock; 45 (top right): NASA/Donaldson Collection/Getty Images; 49 (top right): Fine Art Images/Heritage Images/Getty Images; 52 (top right): Attaphong/Shutterstock; 53 (bottom right): Public Domain; 54 (top left): Kudla/Shutterstock, (top right): Ketpachara Yoosuk/Shutterstock, (centre): Mega Pixel/Shutterstock, (bottom): Stockphoto-graf/Shutterstock; 60 (bottom right): Daniel Prudek/Shutterstock

Every effort has been made to acknowledge correctly and contact the source and/or copyright holder of each picture, and Carlton Books apologises for any unintentional errors or omissions, which will be corrected in future editions of this book.

SCIENCE TECHNOLOGY ENGINEERING MATHS

STEM Activity

AMAZING
MATHS

Hannah Wilson

CARLTON KiDS

CONTENTS

SUPER STEM

Welcome to the world of STEM. STEM stands for science, technology, engineering and maths. These four fabulous subjects open up a world of exciting discovery.

You probably already possess many of the qualities and interests shared by great scientists, technologists, engineers and mathematicians. Read each statement and put a tick in the box if it applies to you.

SCIENCE

YOU...

- are curious about the world around you. ❑

- love to ask questions. ❑

- experiment and try new things, even if it means making a mistake. ❑

You're already on your way to becoming a scientist! You want to find answers to the mysteries of life and understand the world around you.

TECHNOLOGY

YOU...

- are always playing with gadgets. ❑

- like to understand exactly how machines work. ❑

- try to find ways of making everyday tasks easier, such as investigating whether a different route to school makes the journey shorter. ❑

Technology is right up your street! You're fascinated by the latest products and want to find out more about inventions that help to improve our world.

ENGINEERING

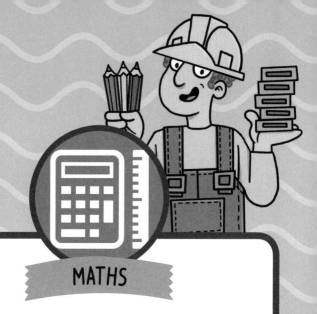

YOU...

- like using your brain to solve problems. ❑

- love playing with construction sets and building bricks. ❑

- enjoy building amazing dens or dams in streams. ❑

You're perfectly suited to a career as an engineer! You could invent or make amazing tools, machines and buildings.

MATHS

YOU...

- like to understand the reasons why something is true. ❑

- often spot patterns such as in pictures or clothing and sequences in numbers like football statistics. ❑

- love 3D puzzles, card games and logic games like chess and battleships. ❑

You're a born mathematician! You're excited by shapes and measurements, and curious to see just what numbers can do when you use them in different ways.

WHAT IS MATHS?

Maths is around us, all the time. We use it to help keep track of the money we spend, score sports matches, calculate quantities for cooking, work out how to build skyscrapers and organise maps.

Maths also reveals the secrets of the natural world – for example, it explains the spiral patterns of seashells and the symmetry of honeycomb.

Numbers are the symbols we use to describe maths. When linked with other symbols, such as + or – and =, they create a unique international language. In this book, we're going to learn how to read and write the language of maths so we can explore and understand the world around us. So, let's get started – we've got shapes to draw, numbers to juggle, codes to decipher, treasure maps to study, computers to program and pizzas to slice!

COOL COLUMNS

A number describes an amount of something. It can be written as a word, like 'eight', or with digits, like '8' or '2'. Digits are a faster way to write a large number. For example, it's much quicker to write '2,917' than it is to write 'two thousand, nine hundred and seventeen'!

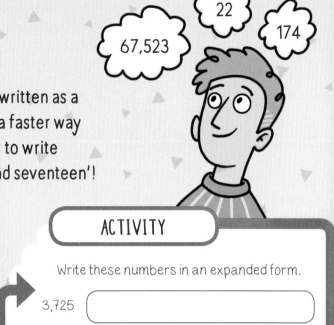

Each digit in a number shows how many you have of a particular value – thousands, hundreds, tens and ones (or units). This is the digit's 'place value'. The columns below show the value of each digit in the number 2,917.

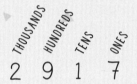

THOUSANDS	HUNDREDS	TENS	ONES
2	9	1	7

There are 2 thousands, 9 hundreds, 1 ten and 7 ones.

We can expand 2,917 so it becomes 2,000 + 900 + 10 + 7.

ACTIVITY

Write these numbers in an expanded form.

3,725

4,159

7,022

ACTIVITY

Can you find your way out of this number maze? Travel from number to number, but make sure the numbers get bigger each time, not smaller!

Look at the numbers you connected to make your way through the maze. How much is added to each one to get the next number in the sequence? What pattern can you see?

CHECK THE ANSWERS AT THE BACK OF THE BOOK!

SUPER SUMS

When adding together numbers, or taking one number away from another, we use symbols to record our maths thinking.

Means 'add on' or 'plus'

Means 'is equal to'

$3 + 2 = 5$

$3 - 2 = 1$

Means 'take away', 'minus' or 'subtract'

You need to know some rules about how to write things down in a calculation!

ORDER RULE: ADDING

When adding, the order of the numbers doesn't matter. You can write the numbers on either side of the + symbol. For example:

$3 + 2 = 5$

$2 + 3 = 5$

ORDER RULE: SUBTRACTING

The order of the numbers **does** matter for subtraction. For example, $3 - 2 = 1$, but if you swap the order so the calculation is $2 - 3$, the answer is not 1!

ACTIVITY

Look at these road signs and work out the distances between the different destinations. All the distances shown are in straight lines.

SCHOOL	2
TRAIN STATION	7
HOSPITAL	10

How many kilometres are there between the school and the train station?

What's the distance between the train station and the hospital?

How far is it from the school to the hospital?

PARK	13
BUS STATION	18
SUPERMARKET	20

How many kilometres are there between the park and the bus station?

What's the distance between the bus station and the supermarket?

How far is it from the park to the supermarket?

CHECK THE ANSWERS AT THE BACK OF THE BOOK!

POPULATION COUNT

The population of the town of Addington is being counted in a survey! Population surveys help make sure that towns like Addington have the right number of services such as schools and hospitals. Help out with the survey by adding up the number of people living in each building.

ADDITION WITH REGROUPING

For tricky addition with numbers that have several digits, organise the numbers in columns according to their place value, like the example below.

```
HUNDREDS  TENS  ONES
            6    7
     +      8    5
     ─────────────────
       1    5    2
            1    1
```

HERE'S HOW TO DO IT:

· Add up the ones first: 7 + 5 = 12.

· Record the digit 2 in the ones column.

· You have created 1 new 'ten', so carry that over into the tens column.

· Now add up the tens, including the 1 that you carried over: 6 + 8 + 1 = 15.

· 15 tens is 1 group of hundreds and 5 tens. Record the 5 in the tens column and carry over the 1 into the hundreds column.

· Now add the hundreds.

· The answer is 152.

ACTIVITY

Add up the number of people living on the first and second floors in each building – and write the total in the space in the bottom of each house.

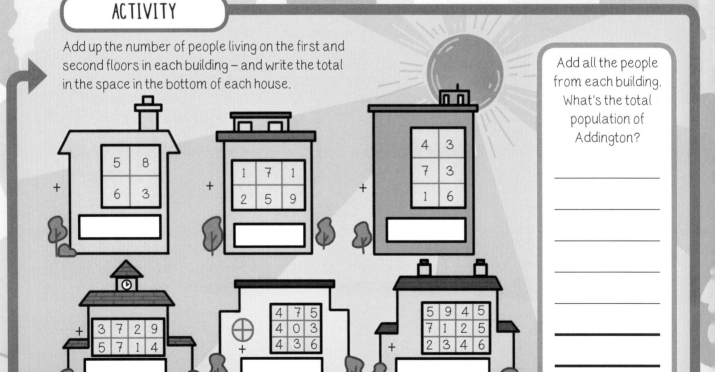

Add all the people from each building. What's the total population of Addington?

_____

_____

_____

_____

_____

_____

CHECK THE ANSWERS AT THE BACK OF THE BOOK!

SUBTRACTION WITH REGROUPING

Welcome to Subtractington! People are moving out of this town. Use column subtraction to work out how many residents are left in each building.

```
  TENS ONES
   8⁄9 ¹2
 -  6 4
 -------
    2 8
```

HERE'S HOW TO DO IT:

· Start with the ones column. 2 − 4 won't work because you can't take 4 ones away from 2. You need to borrow 1 ten from the tens column, so cross out the 9 and reduce it to 8 tens.

· Write the borrowed ten as a 1 next to the 2 in the ones column to make 12 ones. You have now regrouped the 1 ten as 10 ones.

· You can subtract now: 12 − 4 = 8. Record 8 ones in your answer.

· Now work on the tens column: 8 − 6 = 2.

· The answer is 28.

ACTIVITY

Subtract the number of people who are leaving from the number of people who live in each building. Write the answer in the space in the bottom of each house.

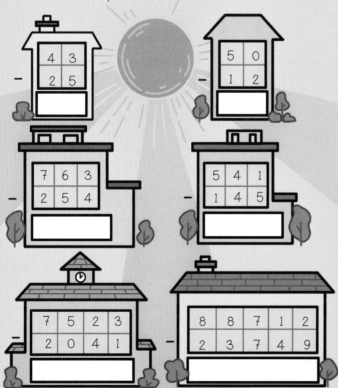

```
  4 3        5 0
- 2 5      - 1 2
```

```
  7 6 3        5 4 1
- 2 5 4      - 1 4 5
```

```
  7 5 2 3        8 8 7 1 2
- 2 0 4 1      - 2 3 7 4 9
```

Add the total remaining residents to figure out the population of Subtractington.

_____

_____

_____

_____

_____

_____

_____

How many more people live in Subtractington than Addington?

_____

_____

_____

11

ABOVE AND BELOW ZERO

Numbers above zero are 'positive'. But if you count down from 10 to zero, you don't need to stop there. Numbers below zero are 'negative' numbers. We show that a number is negative by putting a minus symbol (−) in front of it.

We can use negative numbers when we talk about temperature, which drops below zero when it's very cold. Brrr! In the Antarctic, for example, temperatures struggle to get above −20 degrees Celsius in the summer. Scientists and other support staff live there while they carry out research.

BRAHMAGUPTA

In about AD 628, the Indian mathematician Brahmagupta wrote a book in which he treated zero as a proper number that could be used in calculations. Before, zero had just been used as a symbol to write down when there was no quantity to record, like the zero in 306.

ACTIVITY

Complete this picture of an Antarctic research station by joining the dots – with a twist! The dots have positive and negative numbers. Start at 15 and count down to −15.

ACTIVITY

This thermometer shows the temperature in degrees Celsius (°C). During the day, the temperature goes up and down. Using the information below, write down calculations to work out what temperature the thermometer would show at different times. Use your finger to count up and down the thermometer number line to check your answers.

°C
30
20
10
0
–10
–20

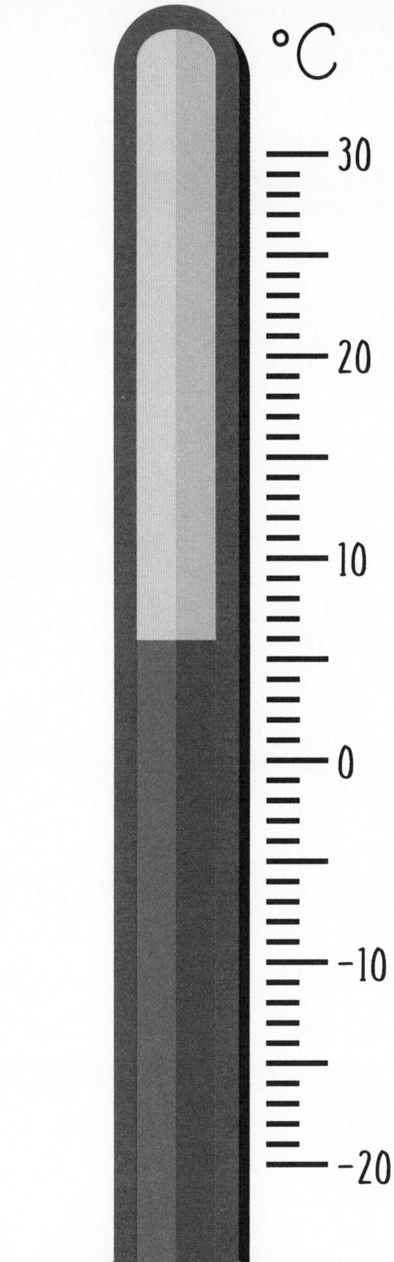

Before dawn, it's a chilly 1°C. The sun rises and the temperature increases by 8 degrees.

At midday, a freak ice storm hits and the temperature drops by 11 degrees.

The sun comes out again in the afternoon and the temperature rises by 5 degrees.

Finally, night falls and the temperature drops by 7 degrees.

DID YOU KNOW?

The lowest ground temperature ever recorded on Earth is –89°C! That was in Antarctica in 1983.

CHECK THE ANSWERS AT THE BACK OF THE BOOK!

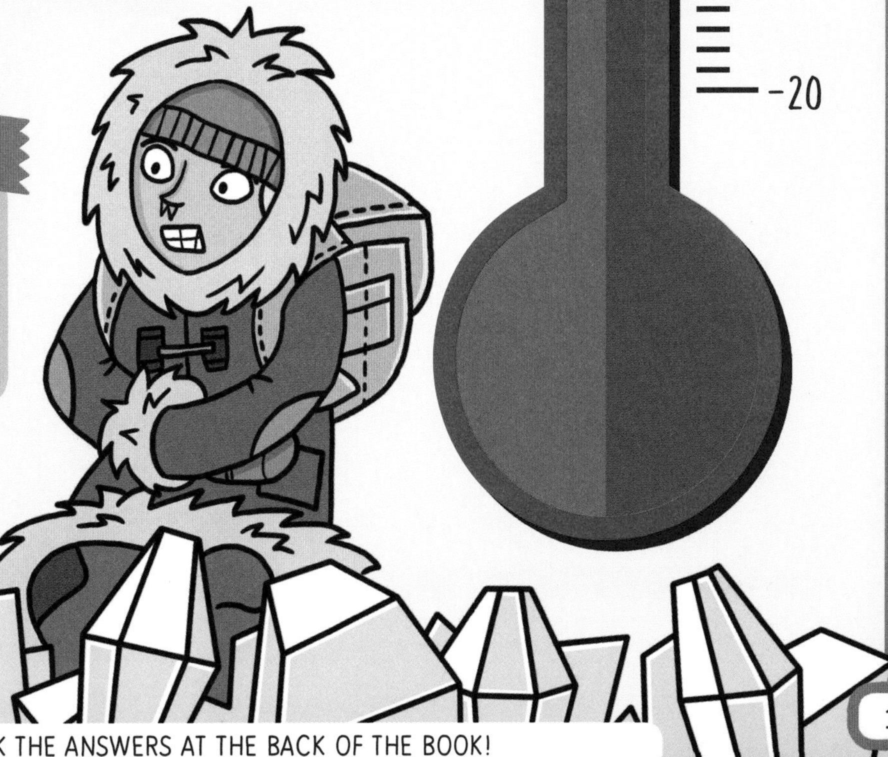

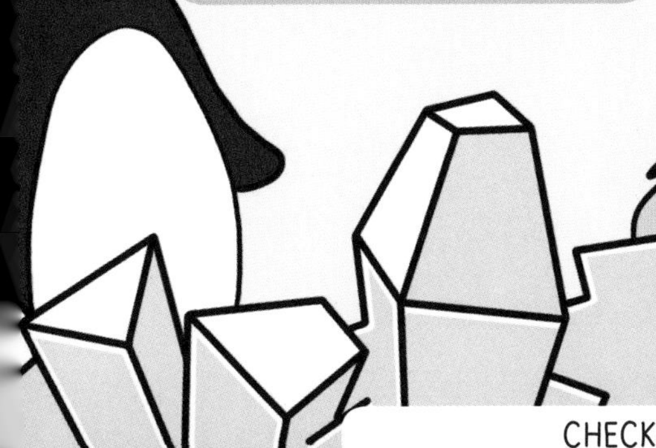

MULTIPLY AND SUPPLY

Meet the 'multiplication' or 'times' symbol: X. Multiplication is very handy if you want to add up the same number many — or multiple — times. If 5 boxes each contain 3 pencils, how many pencils are there in total? To work this out, we need to add 3 + 3 + 3 + 3 + 3 = 15. Or you could use the X symbol to write 5 X 3 = 15.

ORDER RULE: MULTIPLYING

You can multiply numbers in any order. For example:

5 x 3 = 15
3 x 5 = 15

DID YOU KNOW?

On a calculator, computer or smartphone, the multiplication symbol is often *.

ACTIVITY

Your company makes sports equipment. Three orders for packs of equipment have come in. How much does each customer owe?

Multiply the number ordered by the price to calculate the bill.

ORDER	TOTAL PRICE
HOLIDAY CAMP 2 bundles of frisbees	2 x £8 =
SPORTS SHOP 2 crates of basketballs	
SCHOOL 2 tubes of tennis balls	

£7

£8

£9

CHECK THE ANSWERS AT THE BACK OF THE BOOK!

COLUMN MULTIPLICATION

For tricky multiplications with more than one digit,
set out your numbers in columns.

$$\begin{array}{r} 2\ 3 \\ \times \quad 5 \\ \hline 1\ 1\ 5 \\ \hline {\scriptstyle 1} \end{array}$$

· First, multiply the number in the ones column: $3 \times 5 = 15$.
· You have created a new 'ten', so carry the 1 over into the tens column.
· Now multiply the ten value: $2 \times 5 = 10$.
· Add the extra 1 to give 11.
· The answer is 115.

ACTIVITY

The phone rings. The holiday camp wants to double its order, the sports shop wants to triple its order and the school wants to quadruple its order! Use column multiplication to multiply their first bill total by the increased amount.

HOLIDAY CAMP

Total of new bill: £ _____

SPORTS SHOP

Total of new bill: £ _____

SCHOOL

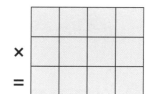

Total of new bill: £ _____

CHECK THE ANSWERS AT THE BACK OF THE BOOK!

MEET THE MULTIPLES

Multiples are a way of counting by a number in a series.
When you count by 5s you're multiplying by 5s.
5, 10, 15, 20 is the same as (5 × 1) = 5, (5 × 2) = 10,
(5 × 3) = 15, and so on. Multiples are useful everywhere,
even shopping.

ACTIVITY

Vera the vet needs food for her animal shelter. Help her count in multiples along each aisle to find the quantities on her shopping list. Circle the boxes as you count, and note the numbers on her shopping list.

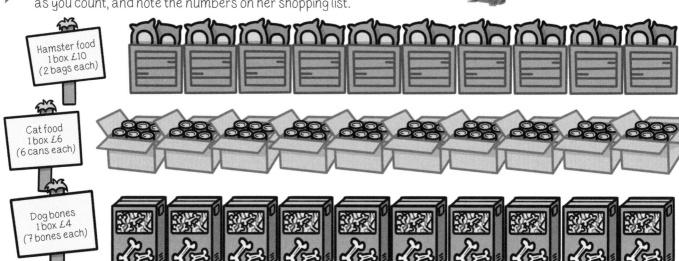

Hamster food
1 box £10
(2 bags each)

Cat food
1 box £6
(6 cans each)

Dog bones
1 box £4
(7 bones each)

SHOPPING LIST

14 bags of hamster food = [   ] boxes of hamster food

30 cans of cat food = [   ] boxes of cat food

42 dog bones = [   ] boxes of dog bones

Put the number of boxes needed in the 'amount' column.
Write the price per item in the price column. Multiply the
amount by the price to get the cost for each type of food.

AMOUNT OF BOXES	PRICE	TOTAL
	GRAND TOTAL:	

Use the multiples of 3 and 8 to find out which animals are hiding in the grassland! Choose a coloured pen and then join the dots, starting at 3 and counting up in multiples of 3.

Then use another colour and start at 8. Join the dots that are multiples of 8.

Finish by colouring the scene.

SHARE AND DIVIDE

If you feel like sharing, the maths you need is division. For this, we use the symbol ÷. This breaks a number into equal amounts. For example, 8 ÷ 2 means divide 8 into 2 equal amounts.

ORDER RULE: DIVIDING

The order of the numbers matters in division calculations.

For example, 8 ÷ 2 = 4, but if you swap the order and write 2 ÷ 8, the answer is not 4!

ACTIVITY

Five friends are getting ready for an outdoor adventure. Three are going fishing and two will make a den.

1   FOOD FOR ALL FIVE FRIENDS

5 water bottles

10 energy bars

55 grapes

15 bananas

2   GEAR FOR THREE FISHERS

12 worms   6 hooks

3   GEAR FOR TWO DEN-MAKERS

26 sticks

6 coils of rope

WRITE A LIST OF ITEMS FOR EACH RUCKSACK HERE

Pack a rucksack for one of the fishers and one of the den-makers. Use division to figure out how much they need of each item. Remember, the snacks are shared by all five friends. The fishing gear is shared by three friends. The den gear is shared by two friends.

FISHER'S RUCKSACK

☐	water bottles
☐	energy bars
☐	grapes
☐	bananas
☐	worms
☐	hooks

DEN-MAKER'S RUCKSACK

☐	water bottles
☐	energy bars
☐	grapes
☐	bananas
☐	sticks
☐	coils of rope

CHECK THE ANSWERS AT THE BACK OF THE BOOK!

COLUMN DIVISION

To divide a large number, put the numbers in columns and divide the hundreds, tens and ones separately. This is the calculation 324 ÷ 2 put into columns:

$$\begin{array}{r} 1\ 6\ 2 \\ 2\overline{)3^{1}2\ 4} \end{array}$$

Start in the hundreds column. The 2 goes into 3 once with 1 left over. We call that 1 'the remainder'. It creates an extra 'ten', so write it in the top of the tens column to make 12.

Keep dividing by 2: 12 divided by 2 is 6 with no remainder. 4 divided by 2 is 2 with no remainder. The answer is 162.

TOP TIP

$$200 \div 10 = 20$$
$$2{,}000 \div 10 = 200$$
$$20{,}000 \div 10 = 2{,}000$$

Do you see a pattern? When you divide by 10, you drop a zero.

When dividing by 100, drop two zeros:

$$200 \div 100 = 2.$$

ACTIVITY

It's time to toast marshmallows on the campfire! The five children have three bags of marshmallows, each containing 26 marshmallows. Use division to share the marshmallows between all five friends.

How many marshmallows are there in total?

How many does each child get if they divide them up equally?

Are there any left over (remainders)? If so, how many?

Five more children arrive. Now there are 10 children to share all the marshmallows. Divide the total by 10. How many will each child get?

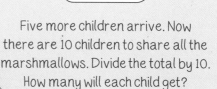

FACTOR FACTORY

The factors of a number are all the numbers that you can multiply together to make that number. So, the factors of 4 are 1 and 4 (1 × 4 = 4) and also 2 (2 × 2 = 4). The factors of 6 are 1, 6, 2 and 3. 1 and 2 are both factors of 4 and of 6, so we call them 'common factors' of 4 and 6.

FACTORS OF 4

1   2   4

ACTIVITY

Work out the factors of 9, 14 and 21 and write them in the key below. Then use the key to colour in the factor factory to find out what it's making!

TOP TIPS

The factors of a number are always 1 and the number itself. But sometimes there are more!

KEY

■ Factors of 9   ☐ ☐ ☐

■ Factors of 14   ☐ ☐ ☐ ☐

■ Factors of 21   ☐ ☐ ☐ ☐

CAN YOU FIND THE HCF?

Look at the factors of 14 and 21. What is the highest factor that they have in common? That's the 'Highest Common Factor' or HCF.

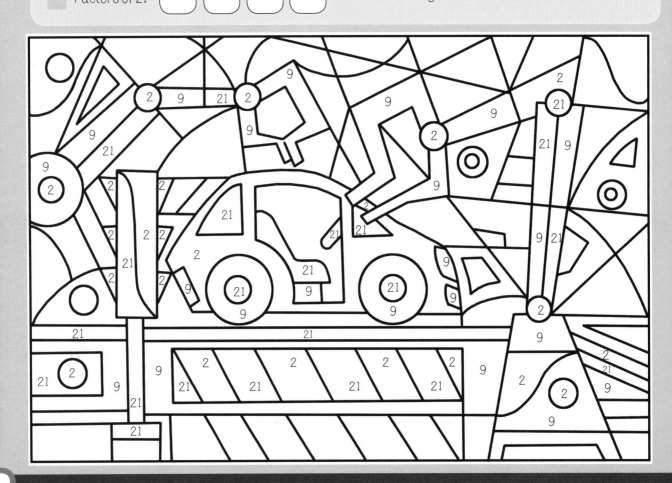

Four teachers are at the bookshop, buying books for their class. The books come in packs of 3, 4, 5 or 7.

Mr 12 needs to buy exactly 12 books. The packs of 3 and 4 books are perfect, because those numbers are factors of 12. Mr 12 could buy four packs of 3 books, or three packs of 4 books. Which option would be cheapest?

Help the other teachers find their factors and compare two different pack options. Circle the cheapest option for each teacher.

MR 12 COULD BUY:	MS 15 COULD BUY:	MR 20 COULD BUY:	MRS 21 COULD BUY:
4 × 3-pack of books	...... × ......-pack of books	...... × ......-pack of books	...... × ......-pack of books
4 × £10 = £......	...... × £...... = £......	...... × £...... = £......	...... × £...... = £......
OR	OR	OR	OR
3 × 4-pack of books	...... × ......-pack of books	...... × ......-pack of books	...... × ......-pack of books
3 × £12 = £......	...... × £...... = £......	...... × £...... = £......	...... × £...... = £......

NUMBERS IN THEIR PRIME

A prime number is a number that can be divided only by itself and 1.
For example, 17 can only be divided by 17 and 1, so 17 is a prime number.
A composite number is a number that can be divided by several numbers.
For example, 20 can be divided by 2, 4, 5 and 10 as well as
20 and 1, so 20 is a composite number.

ACTIVITY

The fish in this pond are either composite or prime numbers. Help Costas and Priya catch the composite numbers by colouring them in. Use the Top Tips box to help you!

TOP TIPS

All numbers ending in 5 are composite.
All even numbers are composite except 2.
All numbers that can be divided by 3 are composite except 3 itself.

CHECK THE ANSWERS AT THE BACK OF THE BOOK!

This fussy caterpillar eats only prime numbers up to 50! They are 2, 3, 5, 7, 11, 13, 17, 19, 23, 29, 31, 37, 41, 43 and 47.

Draw a line linking up the prime numbers and help it munch its way through the leaf maze.

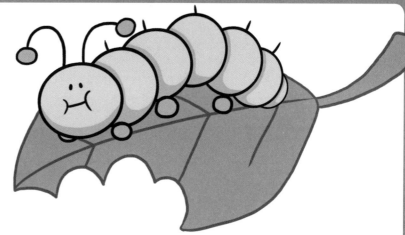

START

2	35	10	14	18	27	9	8	28	50
3	5	7	11	4	39	38	6	20	30
24	34	22	13	23	29	31	40	33	46
32	48	21	17	19	23	37	41	43	45
25	26	44	42	36	49	1	16	47	15

FINISH

DID YOU KNOW?

The number 1 is neither a prime number nor a composite!

Some cicadas leave their burrows to lay eggs every 7, 13 or 17 years. They may choose these prime-number intervals to avoid predators, whose life-cycles are not based on primes.

CRACK THE CODE

A code is a sequence of numbers. We use codes every day in lots of different ways — for example, in the passcode on our phone, the lock on our bike or the barcodes on products. But not all codes are random sequences of numbers. Many are based on maths and number patterns.

ACTIVITY

A cyber-criminal has hacked into the city bank's computers and transferred all the money to his own account. It's your job to crack the codes. Solve each challenge and use the encryption key on the next page to find out who the villain is.

1

Write the next number in these sequences.

23, 27, 31, 35, 39, ☐

1, 2, 4, 8, 16, ☐

20, 15, 11, 8, 6, ☐

12, 24, 36, 48, 60, ☐

2

Read the riddle below. Which of the three padlocks is it describing?

What do the three numbers on the correct padlock add up to?

_____

My second number is double the first. My third is half the first.

3

HINT
The dial always cuts through numbers which are opposite each other.

The line on this clock face cuts through 12 and 6, whose sum total is 18. Rotate the line until you find two numbers on the clock face whose sum total is divisible by 7.

What is the sum total of the two numbers that ☐ is divisible by 7?

Which two numbers make this total? ☐ ☐

Use this answer in the encryption key.

CHECK THE ANSWERS AT THE BACK OF THE BOOK!

4

The Fibonacci sequence is a famous code. It starts like this:

1, 1, 2, 3, 5, 8, 13...

Can you work out the pattern?

Think about how each number is related to the two numbers before it.

What's the next number in the sequence?

5

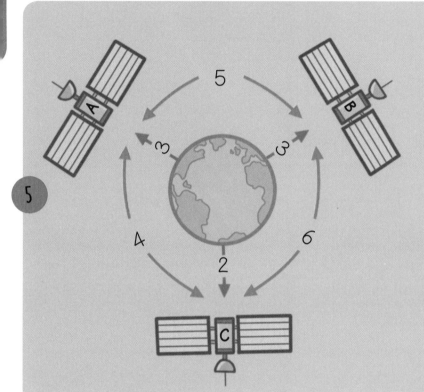

This picture shows how many seconds it takes for messages from Earth to reach different satellites and travel between them.

What is the quickest route for a message to leave your computer on Earth, travel to all three satellites and arrive back on Earth? How long will it take?

Shortest route:

Time taken:

NOW DISCOVER THE CRIMINAL'S NAME!

A	B	C	D	E	F	G	H	I	J	K	L	M
12	3	21	10	8	37	15	22	32	41	17	5	29

N	O	P	Q	R	S	T	U	V	W	X	Y	Z
74	14	4	24	7	16	1	49	63	43	2	72	61

Use the encryption key above to turn the number answers from each challenge into letters, and discover the thief's name.

CHALLENGE 1

CHALLENGE 2

CHALLENGE 3

CHALLENGE 4

CHALLENGE 5

FOOD FRACTIONS

A fraction describes how a whole number is divided into equal parts. The biscuit on the right is divided into three parts. If you eat 2 parts, you've eaten 2/3 (two thirds) of the biscuit.

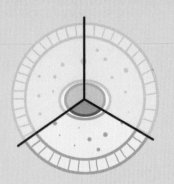

$\frac{2}{3}$

← Numerator — the number of parts we're talking about

← Line means 'divided by'

← Denominator — the number of parts in the whole

ACTIVITY

Three friends are sharing a pizza. There are 12 slices, but each person wants a different amount of pizza. How much does each person get? Colour in the slices, using a different colour for each person.

CHUN
Just ³/₁₂ for me.

SANJAY
I'll have ²/₁₂ please.

If a pizza is divided into 12 slices and we eat all 12 slices, we have eaten ¹²/₁₂ of the pizza – that's the whole pizza. So, if the numerator and denominator are the same number, that fraction equals 1.

$^4/_4 = 1$,

$^{11}/_{11} = 1$,

$^{433}/_{433} = 1$,

and so on.

RUBY
I would like ⁶/₁₂ of the pizza.

How many slices are left? Write your answer as a fraction.

CHECK THE ANSWERS AT THE BACK OF THE BOOK!

EQUIVALENT FRACTIONS

Ruby ate 6 out of 12 slices. That was ½ the pizza. It's the same amount of pizza, but broken into fewer pieces because the denominator is smaller.

To simplify a fraction, divide the numerator and denominator by the same number.
So, ⁶/₁₂ = ½. They are 'equivalent fractions'.

$$\frac{6}{12} \overset{\div 6}{\underset{\div 6}{=}} \frac{1}{2}$$

This also works in reverse. You can multiply the numerator and the denominator of a fraction by the same nymber and get an equivalent fraction.

$$\frac{1}{2} \overset{\times 6}{\underset{\times 6}{=}} \frac{6}{12}$$

ACTIVITY

Each squirrel is looking for a route up the tree that matches his fraction.
Draw a route up the tree for each squirrel, following their equivalent fractions.

Which nut will the ½ squirrel get?

Which nut will the ⅓ squirrel get?

Which nut will the ¼ squirrel get?

DECIMALS THAT DIVIDE

Like fractions, decimals describe how a whole number is divided into parts. A decimal number contains a decimal point that separates the whole number and its fractional parts. Each part is one tenth ($1/10$) of the previous unit. The decimal to the right of the decimal point is $1/10$ and is written as 0.1. If you divide that tenth into another 10 parts, each of the smaller parts is one hundredth ($1/100$). This is written as 0.01.

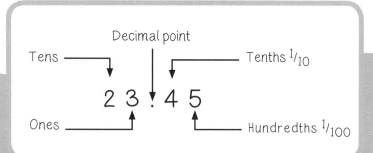

EQUIVALENTS

$0.5 = 5/10 = 1/2$

$0.25 = 25/100 = 1/4$

$0.75 = 75/100 = 3/4$

ACTIVITY

Draw rope bridges between the posts that have equivalent numbers to cross the gorge. One has been done for you already.

CHECK THE ANSWERS AT THE BACK OF THE BOOK!

To add decimals, line up the decimal points. Then add each unit. Use regrouping if you need it.

Try out addition with decimals. Add up the cost of your shopping. Write down the cost for each item. Make sure the decimal points line up. Then work out the total cost of your shopping.

£0.50 £2.30
£1.50 £0.30 £0.40
£0.15 £1.75 £0.75

	TENS	ONES		TENTHS	HUNDREDTHS
BREAD			.		
APPLE			.		
MILK			.		
CHEESE			.		
CEREAL			.		
GARLIC			.		
BROCCOLI			.		
PASTA			.		
TOTAL			.		

You pay for the shopping with a £10 note. How much change would you get?

There are 100 pence (p) in £1, so the decimal system is perfect for writing amounts of money.

If you have £2 and 53p, it's written as £2.53, because in addition to 2 whole pounds, you have 53 hundredths of 1 pound.

If you have only 2p, that's £0.02 or 2 hundredths of a pound. You don't have any whole pounds.

29

PERCENTAGES

Percentages, like fractions and decimals, describe part of a whole number.
Per cent (%) means 'out of 100'. So, 50% means 50 out of 100 or $^{50}/_{100}$.

ACTIVITY

When you receive data on your computer or phone, it doesn't arrive as a whole package. It is broken into pieces. Your device tells you how much of the whole package you have received. The messages below come in 10 parts. Colour in the loading screens to match the percentages.

HINT: You don't have to colour in whole squares.

Halfway there!
LOADING...50%

Thanks for waiting!
LOADING...25%

Almost fully loaded!
LOADING...90%

Not long now!
LOADING...75%

CHECK THE ANSWERS AT THE BACK OF THE BOOK!

Connect each flag with the correct boat.

50% GIRLS
25% BOYS
25% DOGS

20% DOGS
50% GIRLS
30% BOYS

50% DOGS
25% GIRLS
25% BOYS

ACTIVITY

Draw lines to connect each food item with the right percentage, decimal and fraction to show how much food and drink there is.

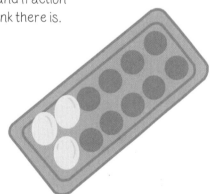

25%

$25/100 = 1/4$

0.25

75%

$75/100 = 3/4$

0.75

50%

$5/10 = 1/2$

0.5

CHECK THE ANSWERS AT THE BACK OF THE BOOK!

WHAT'S THE TIME?

What time do you get up? What time does school start? When do you need to be at the dentist's? How many hours until the party starts? Getting anywhere on time means learning how to read a clock!

REMEMBER, THERE ARE:

60 seconds in a minute

60 minutes in an hour

24 hours in a day – 12 in the morning (a.m.) and 12 in the afternoon, evening and night (p.m.).

TOP TIPS

The long hand on an analogue clock points to the minute and the short hand points to the hour.

Minutes are grouped together in sets of five.

Often we say '**quarter past** seven' when we mean 15 minutes past seven. This is because 15 minutes is $\frac{1}{4}$ of 60 minutes, a quarter of an hour. '**Quarter to** seven' means 15 minutes **before** seven.

'**Half past** seven' means 30 minutes past seven – $\frac{1}{2}$ of 60 minutes.

Draw the hands on the clocks to keep track of time during this busy day.

1 Wakey, wakey! It's 7 o'clock in the morning.

2 Eat breakfast at half past seven.

3 Catch the bus at quarter past eight.

4 School starts at quarter to nine.

8 Hungry? Lunch is at 1:00.

14 Lights out at 8:35. Goodnight!

7 Swimming lesson at quarter to twelve.

9 Soccer match at 2:40 p.m.

6 Head to the playground for break at 10:15 a.m.

13 Read a book in bed at five past eight.

10 Start homework at twenty minutes to four.

5 It's half past nine – time for a maths lesson!

$2 + 12 \div 3 \times 5 =$

11 Eat dinner at 6:15 p.m.

12 It's half past seven. Jump in the bath.

CHECK THE ANSWERS AT THE BACK OF THE BOOK!

ROMAN NUMERALS

The ancient Romans used letter symbols to represent numbers. We still sometimes use these Roman numerals, especially on clock faces.

ROMAN RULES

For smaller numbers, you just need to recognise three letter symbols:

1 = I   5 = V   10 = X

When a smaller number appears after a larger one, add the two together: VI = 5 + 1, so VI = 6. XI is 11.

When a smaller number appears before a larger one, subtract the smaller number from the larger one: IV = 5 − 1, so IV is 4. IX is 9.

You can write all the numbers between 1 and 49 in Roman numerals using just these three symbols.

20 = XX	60 = LX	100 = C
30 = XXX	70 = LXX	500 = D
40 = XL	80 = LXXX	1000 = M
50 = L	90 = XC	

ACTIVITY

Help the soldier find his way back to camp by following Roman numerals in increasing order from I to XX. Beware of dead ends!

ACTIVITY

Roman numerals were hard to use in calculations, because there were no columns for thousands, hundreds, tens and ones – and no zeros! For two thousand, the Romans simply wrote M twice: MM. This meant that simple numbers could be really long!

The numbers below are years shown in Roman numerals. Can you figure out the year that they represent? Use the box on page 34 to help you.

1 MMX ⬚

2 MMXXIX ⬚

3 MMLXIV ⬚

Today, we use the Hindu-Arabic number system to write '2000' – a number that's easy to write and easy to use in calculations like adding and subtracting.

ACTIVITY

Below are historical events. Write each year in Roman numerals. Then find the year in the grid and circle it. The first one is done for you.

1 The city of Rome was founded in 753 BCE.
DCCLIII

2 The Great Fire of Rome took place in AD 64.
⬚

3 Rome's Colosseum was completed in about AD 80.
⬚

4 Rome split into Eastern and Western empires in AD 395.
⬚

C	D	T	I	R	E	V	S	G	J	J	K	K
M	N	X	H	I	V	X	I	V	F	D	X	Z
O	P	C	L	K	M	J	U	H	N	E	B	Y
T	G	F	V	L	D	E	R	V	X	H	F	V
D	S	X	C	U	Y	H	J	N	B	G	T	F
V	F	R	D	C	C	L	I	I	I	B	O	P
L	M	N	W	B	V	C	X	Z	A	S	D	F
G	X	H	Q	I	V	X	R	V	T	L	D	E
V	I	X	Q	O	P	V	L	X	K	X	I	M
N	X	I	L	V	F	D	C	W	X	S	Z	M
Q	E	W	U	U	I	V	J	K	U	Y	G	L
R	F	C	E	X	I	Q	A	I	X	V	V	X
N	M	C	H	G	F	U	Y	I	O	I	L	I
J	M	C	H	G	M	L	X	X	X	C	V	V
W	Q	X	S	X	Z	X	C	V	C	B	N	M
J	K	C	I	V	U	C	P	K	J	L	H	N
B	G	V	V	C	D	R	E	S	D	X	C	X

MEASURING MAYHEM

Length can be measured in units called millimetres (mm), centimetres (cm) and metres (m). Grams (g) and kilograms (kg) are used to measure weight. In this system, called the 'metric' system, each unit of measurement increases or decreases in multiples of ten. Special prefixes like 'kilo' and 'deci' show the value of each measurement unit.

There is a clever way to remember the order of these units as they increase or decrease by factors of ten. Just remember '**King Henry Died By Drinking Chocolate Milkshakes**'.

KILO	HECTO	DECA	BASE UNIT	DECI	CENTI	MILLI
10 × 10 × 10 × LARGER than the base unit	10 × 10 × LARGER than the base unit	10 × LARGER than the base unit	METRE LITRE GRAM	10 × SMALLER than the base unit	10 × 10 × SMALLER than the base unit	10 × 10 × 10 × SMALLER than the base unit
1 kilo = 1,000 base units	1 hecto = 100 base units	1 deca = 10 base units	1 unit	10 deci = 1 unit	100 centi = 1 unit	1,000 milli = 1 unit

To convert larger units to smaller units, use multiplication. For example, to convert metres to centimetres, multiply the number of base units you have by 100 (10 × 10):

4 METRES = 4 × 100 (OR 10 × 10) = 400 CENTIMETRES

To convert smaller units to larger units, use division. For example, to convert metres to kilometres, divide the number of base units by 1,000 (10 × 10 × 10):

4,000 METRES = 4 ÷ 1,000 (OR 10 × 10 × 10) = 4 KILOMETRES

MULTIPLY — DECIMAL TO THE RIGHT

DIVIDE — DECIMAL TO THE LEFT

Use a short cut! Convert units by moving the decimal to the right (to reach smaller units) or to the left (to reach larger units). To divide, move the decimal to the left. To multiply, move the decimal to the right.

Divide / multiply by 10	Divide / multiply by 100	Divide / multiply by 1,000
Move decimal 1 time	Move decimal 2 times	Move decimal 3 times

These builders are struggling with different units of measurement. Choose the correct size of each item they need in order to finish the house.

Circle the correct door, window and roof beam that will fit.

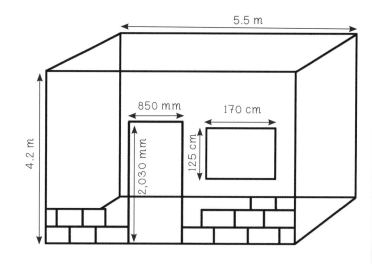

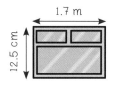

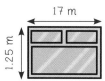

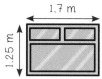

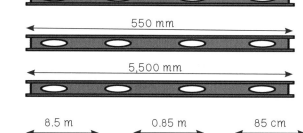

How many rows of bricks will the builder need to lay from the bottom to the top of the house?

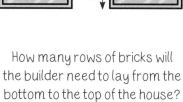

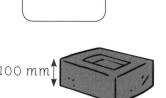

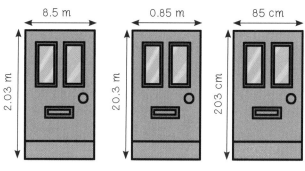

ACTIVITY

These three bags of sand need to be unloaded by order of weight.

Fill in the missing weight conversions on the bags. Then write down the order the bags should be unloaded in, from heaviest to lightest.

A

1000 g
=
.... kg

B

.... g
=
10 kg

C

.... g
=
0.1 kg

1

2

3

SPORTS DAY

Can you imagine a sports competition without numbers? It would be chaos!
Without maths, there would be no way of measuring how far someone had run,
jumped or thrown. We wouldn't be able to compare speeds or heights or distances.
We'd never know if someone had beaten their personal best or set a new world record.

ACTIVITY

These athletes are busy running, jumping and throwing. Use your maths
skills to help them take part in the competition and sort out the results!

HURDLES

There's only one hurdle on the
track! Add the other hurdles
by drawing one every seven
metres in all three lanes.

JAVELIN

Five athletes are competing in the
javelin. Read the following report,
then draw their javelins flying
through the air and landing at the
correct distances. Use colours to
match each athlete's vest.

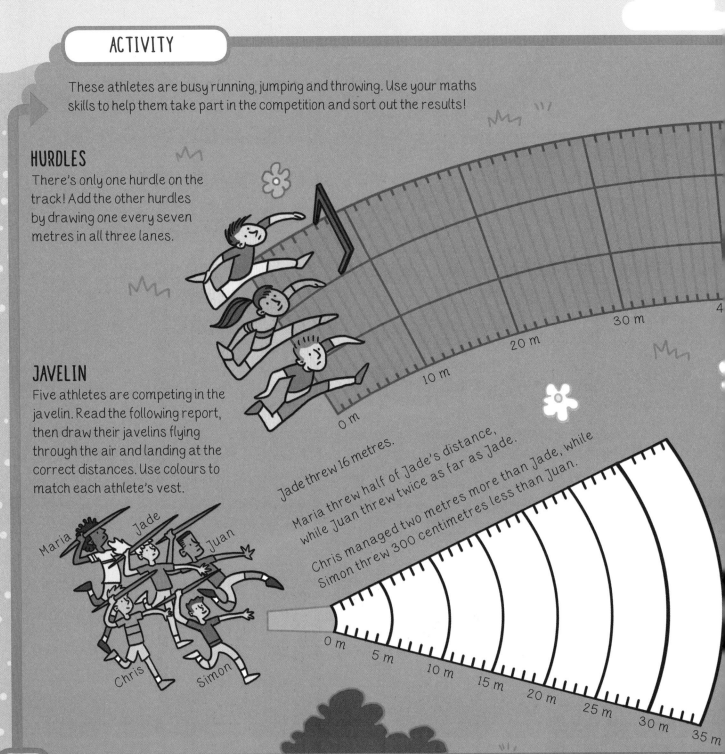

Jade threw 16 metres.

Maria threw half of Jade's distance,
while Juan threw twice as far as Jade.

Chris managed two metres more than Jade, while
Simon threw 300 centimetres less than Juan.

CHECK THE ANSWERS AT THE BACK OF THE BOOK!

1st, 2nd, 3rd, etc. are **ordinal** numbers. Ordinals indicate a position in relation to something else. These ordinals let the runners know what order, or position, they finished the race in.

SPRINT

Rank these runners according to their race results to show who came 1st, 2nd, 3rd, 4th, 5th and 6th.

SPRINT: RESULTS		
Name	Time (seconds)	Position
Lucy	14.32	
Amir	14.23	
Alexander	14.01	
Rosa	14.10	
Tariq	14.31	
Imani	14.13	

HALF MARATHON

In the half marathon, the first three runners to cross the line receive medals. Convert their finishing times to hours, minutes and seconds. Then colour their medals gold, silver or bronze!

HALF MARATHON: RESULTS		
Name	Time	Time in hours, minutes, seconds
Salma	79 minutes 22 seconds	...... h ...... m ...... s
Zara	125 minutes 51 seconds	...... h ...... m ...... s
Ben	120 minutes 30 seconds	...... h ...... m ...... s

BEN

SALMA

ZARA

39

CHECK THE ANSWERS AT THE BACK OF THE BOOK!

WILDLIFE WATCH

Keeping track of data is one of the most important jobs a scientist has. Data has to be accurate so that people can trust the outcome of experiments. To help us keep track of data, and to compare and analyse it, we often present it in charts, tables or pictograms.

ACTIVITY

Check out this one month survey of wildlife on a nature reserve in the Amazon rainforest. Now you have all your data, you need to work out what it means! This table shows how many sloths, snakes and butterflies were spotted in the four different areas of the reserve.

	Sloths	Snakes	Butterflies
North	2	15	65
South	0	11	97
East	4	23	124
West	0	18	56

How many snakes did you spot in the eastern area?

How many creatures in total did you spot in the northern area?

How many sloths did you see in the whole reserve?

Which animal is the most common?

ACTIVITY

This chart shows what a group of monkeys ate in one day. One picture in the chart equals four food items in real life.

 = 4 passion fruits

 = 4 nuts

 = 4 leaves

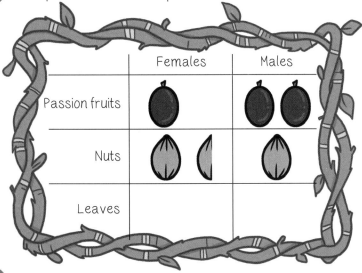

	Females	Males
Passion fruits		
Nuts		
Leaves		

How many passion fruits did the male monkeys eat?

How many nuts did the females eat?

How many passion fruits were eaten altogether?

How many passion fruits and nuts did the females eat altogether?

Fill in the correct amount of leaf symbols to show that the females ate 12 leaves and the males ate 10.

CHECK THE ANSWERS AT THE BACK OF THE BOOK!

ACTIVITY

In this chart, a researcher charted birds for one week. Every time she saw one bird, she drew a straight line. For the fifth bird, she drew a diagonal line through the other four lines. This groups five together so she can count her total numbers by five.

On Thursday the data was left off. She saw six green parrots and 12 blue ones. Mark the tally in the chart.

How many green parrots were charted on Wednesday? ⬭

On which day did the scientist record the most blue parrots? ⬭

How many parrots in total were observed on the weekend? ⬭

How many green parrots were recorded altogether? ⬭

	Green parrots	Blue parrots
Monday	卌	卌 II
Tuesday	卌 卌 卌 III	卌 卌 II
Wednesday	卌 卌 I	II
Thursday		
Friday	卌 卌 卌 卌 I	卌 卌 卌 II
Saturday	III	卌 I
Sunday	卌 II	II

ACTIVITY

A pie chart shows how one large group is divided up. The whole pie represents the whole group, or 100%. One half represents 50% and a quarter is 25%.

This pie chart shows how the reserve's population of river animals is divided into different species. Choose a colour for each animal type and colour in the key, then colour the pie chart to show the correct proportions.

Complete this pie chart and key to show how the reserve's parrot population is divided up. Half of them are green parrots, one quarter are blue and one quarter are red.

KEY

☐ 50% fish

☐ 25% reptiles

☐ 25% amphibians

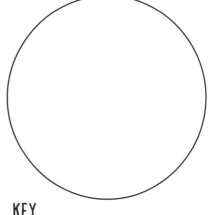

KEY

☐ 50% ⬭

☐ 25% ⬭

☐ 25% ⬭

FIRST-RATE RATIOS

Ratios help us compare amounts. If the ratio of emperor penguins to Adélie penguins on an iceberg is 1:2, it means that for every one emperor penguin, there are two Adélie penguins. So if the iceberg is home to 10 emperor penguins, there would be 20 Adélie penguins. 10:20 is the same ratio as 1:2, but ten times bigger.

RATIO RULES

To keep the same ratio, multiply both sides of the ratio by the same number.

 :

x10   x10

$$\text{x10} \;\; 1:2 \;\; \text{x10}$$
$$=$$
$$\text{x10} \;\; 10:20 \;\; \text{x10}$$

  :

ACTIVITY

Draw the correct number of animals for each ratio.

1 RATIO OF TIGERS TO LIONS
2:3

 :

 :

2 RATIO OF ANTS TO BEETLES
4:2

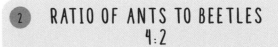

 :

3 RATIO OF SEALS TO SHARKS
3:1

 :

 :

42

CHECK THE ANSWERS AT THE BACK OF THE BOOK!

Recipes use ratios to combine great tastes in just the right amounts.
Write down a ratio for each pair of ingredients.
The first ingredient is provided on the shelf. Choose the correct amount
of the second ingredient to get the recipe just right, and circle it.

INGREDIENTS FOR THAI RED CURRY

4 parts coconut milk to 1 part water

coconut milk : water

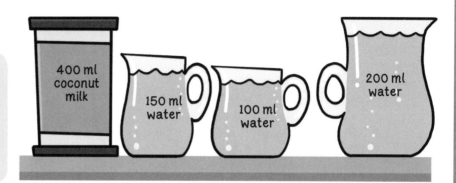

3 parts chilli powder to 4 parts coriander powder

chilli powder : coriander powder

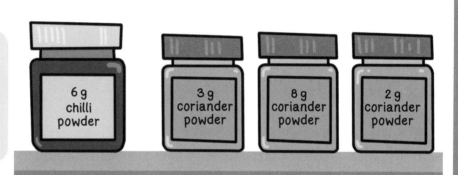

2 part green beans to 3 parts red pepper

green beans : red pepper

3 times as many cloves of garlic as whole onions

cloves of garlic : whole onions

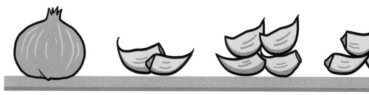

1 whole onion   2 cloves garlic   4 cloves garlic   3 cloves garlic

TREASURE HUNT

Maps are a form of graph with vertical and horizontal lines. These lines are numbered by a horizontal x axis and a vertical y axis. A coordinate pinpoints where the lines cross each other. Coordinates are very useful for finding out where things are!

Coordinate numbers are always listed as:

(X-AXIS NUMBER, Y-AXIS NUMBER)

For example, on the map below the tower sits at coordinate (7, 10), which is 7 on the x axis and 10 on the y axis.

ACTIVITY

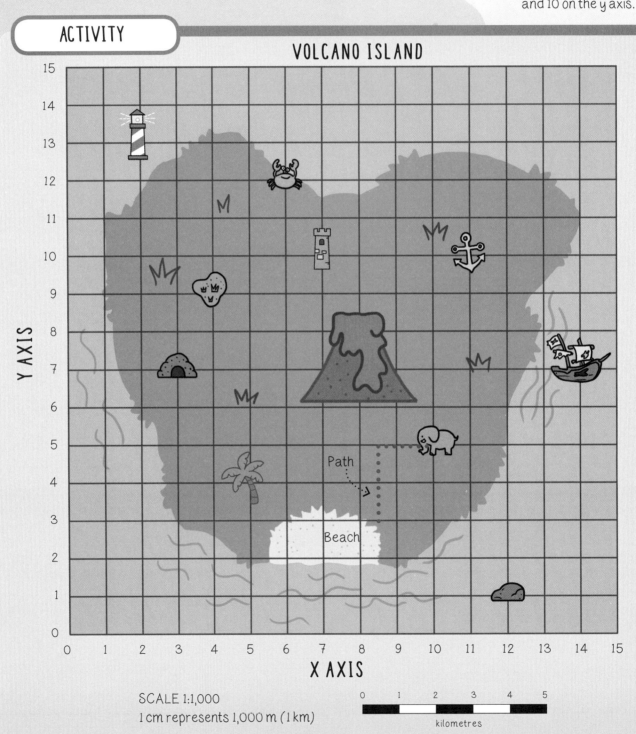

VOLCANO ISLAND

Y AXIS

X AXIS

Path

Beach

SCALE 1:1,000
1 cm represents 1,000 m (1 km)

0 1 2 3 4 5

kilometres

1 Look at the Volcano Island map. Find these coordinate points on the map and write down what feature can be found there. Remember, the first number is the x coordinate, and the second is the y coordinate.

(8,8) [_____]

(10,5) [_____]

(11,10) [_____]

(6,12) [_____]

2 Take the first letter of each answer above. Unscramble the letters to figure out a clue about where a hidden treasure can be found.

[_____]

Now write down the coordinates for the buried treasure: [_____]

3 Now write down the coordinates for these things:

Palm tree [_____]

Sea rock [_____]

Swamp [_____]

Lighthouse [_____]

KATHERINE JOHNSON

As you work out coordinates by counting along the map, think about when humans had to perform long, complicated maths calculations themselves, before computers. American mathematician Katherine Johnson (born in 1918), worked for NASA, calculating the flight paths of spacecraft by hand. She loved to count: 'Anything that could be counted, I did.'

4 A scale bar gives a ratio that shows the relationship between the unit on the map and the actual measurement of the area in the real world.

Find the scale bar on the map opposite. It shows that one square on the map represents 1,000 m (1 km) in real life. Each square of the grid is 1 cm wide. Use it to work out the answers to these questions. Write your answers in kilometres.

How long is the beach?

[_____]

How wide is the island from west to east at its widest point?

[_____]

How long is the path between the beach and the elephant statue?

[_____]

How far is it from the tower to the anchor?

[_____]

PERFECT POLYGONS

A polygon is a flat shape with at least three straight sides. A vertice is where two sides meet on a polygon. Flat shapes are 2D, which means that they have two dimensions — length and width.

ACTIVITY

Fill in the key below. Then use it to colour the polygons in the picture to find out which animal is hiding in the jungle.

KEY	How many sides?	How many vertices?
▲ Triangle		
■ Square		
▬ Rectangle		

	How many sides?	How many vertices?
⬟ Pentagon		
⬡ Hexagon		

A quadrilateral is a polygon with 4 sides.
Which 2 polygons on this page are quadrilaterals?

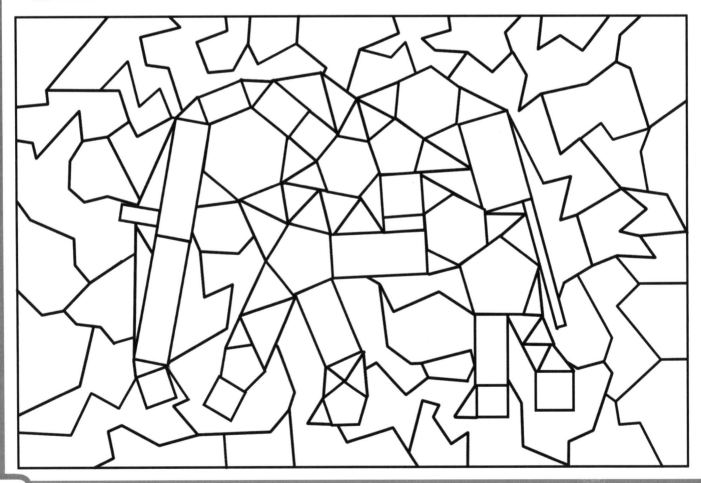

CHECK THE ANSWERS AT THE BACK OF THE BOOK!

UNDERSTANDING AREA

Area is the amount of space inside a polygon. Imagine the area of a rectangle or square as the number of equal-sized or identical squares that would fit inside it.

To calculate the area, multiply the width by the length. For example, this rectangle is 2 squares wide by 4 squares long. Its area is 2 × 4 = 8 squares. Count them up to check!

Length = 4

Width = 2

ACTIVITY

Welcome to Rectangle Farm! Fill in the two missing field lengths, then complete the calculation in each field to solve the area.

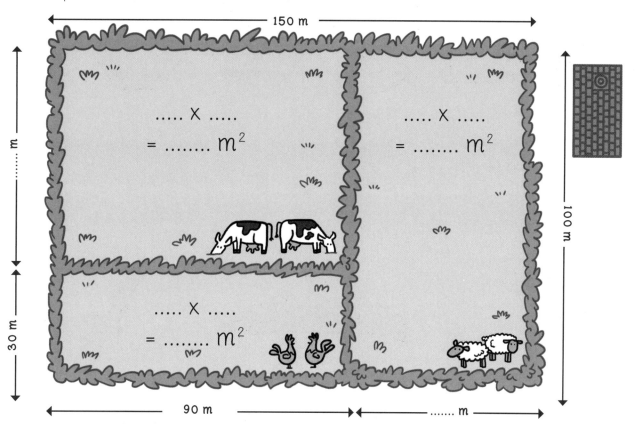

150 m

..... X .....

= .... m^2

..... X .....

= .... m^2

..... X .....

= .... m^2

...... m

m

30 m

90 m

.... m

100 m

What is the total area of the farm? Add the area of each field to find out.

Perimeter is the distance around the edge of a shape. It's the total length of all the sides. The farmer needs new fencing for the perimeter of the whole farm. How much does she need? Add the lengths of each side to find out.

SUPER SYMMETRY

A line of symmetry divides a shape into two identical halves.
Each half is the mirror-image of the other.

ACTIVITY

Draw lines of symmetry on to each of these everyday objects. We've done the first one for you.

Triangle   Square   Pentagon   Hexagon   Heptagon   Octagon

ACTIVITY

Which of these bird shapes is not symmetrical?

CHECK THE ANSWERS AT THE BACK OF THE BOOK!

Complete these images. Make some symmetrical and others not!

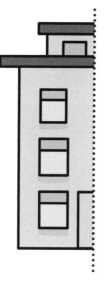

ARCHIMEDES

Geometry is the study of shapes. The great Greek mathematician Archimedes (c.287–212 BCE) made many breakthroughs in geometry, including how to measure the surface area of a sphere (ball). He would work for days – drawing diagrams and scribbling theories – without stopping to eat, drink or wash!

PIECES OF PI

A circle is a closed shape. But it is not a polygon because it has no straight sides. The unique nature of a circle is explained with a special number known as pi. (Sorry — you can't eat this pi!)

Whatever the size of a circle, if you divide its circumference by its diameter, the answer is always an infinite number called pi. Pi is 3.14159.... This number is named after the Greek letter 'p' and its symbol is π.

▬▬ Radius

▬▬ Diameter (2 x radius)

▬▬ The distance around around the edge of a circle is called the **circumference**.

TOP TIP

We use rounding to make it easier to do calculations using pi. Pi is usually rounded to the nearest hundredth: 3.14.

ACTIVITY

If you know the diameter of a circle, you can use pi to work out its circumference:

CIRCUMFERENCE = DIAMETER × π

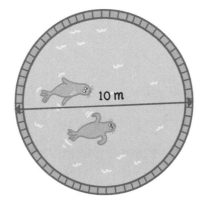

10 m

At the zoo, the seals live in a pool that is surrounded by a circular fence. We know that the diameter of the circle is 10 m. So, in the formula, we can substitute the numbers we know:

CIRCUMFERENCE = 10 × 3.14 = 31.4 m

At the zoo, the fences around the penguin and crocodile pools need to be replaced. What's the circumference of each pool? Use a calculator to multiply if you need help.

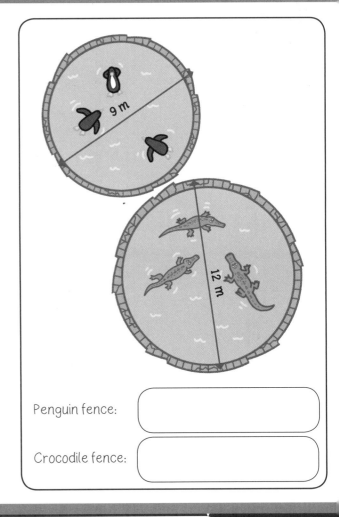

9 m

12 m

Penguin fence: [ ]

Crocodile fence: [ ]

CHECK THE ANSWERS AT THE BACK OF THE BOOK!

You are in charge of a mission to send rockets to circumnavigate three planets, to learn more about each of them. To do this, you'll need to use circumference to calculate the rockets' paths around the planets Zog, Zag and Zig.

The radius of a circle is the distance in a straight line from the centre to the outside edge. So, the radius is half the diameter, or:

DIAMETER = RADIUS × 2

ZOG — 900 km

ZAG — 2,000 km

ZIG — 2,500 km

ROCKET A
Fuel capacity to travel 3,000 km.

ROCKET B
Fuel capacity to travel 8,000 km.

ROCKET C
Fuel capacity to travel 7,000 km.

Calculate and record the circumference trajectory that each rocket would have to fly in order to fly around each planet on its research mission. Then pick the rocket with the right amount of fuel to complete the mission.

	ZOG	ZAG	ZIG
Circumference (Diameter x π)			
Assigned rocket			

51

AWESOME ANGLES

An angle is the space between two crossing lines.
We measure angles in units called degrees (°).
There are 360° in a circle.

A protractor measures angles.

Protractors are very useful objects. You can use them to measure angles in shapes like triangles, squares – even cakes!

In this cake, a large piece is missing. You can see from the numbers marked on the protractor that the angle of the missing piece is 90°.

The angle of the remaining cake is 270°.

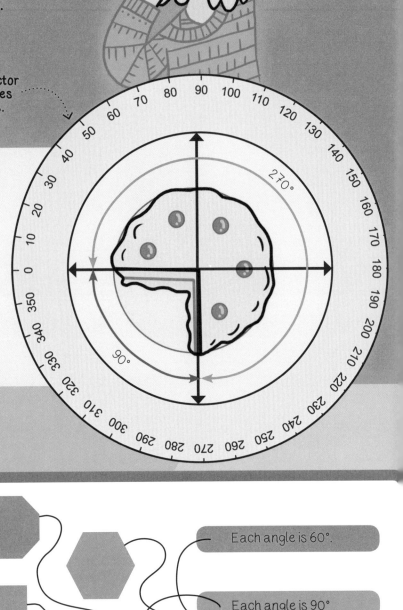

ACTIVITY

The angles inside regular polygons are different depending on the shape. Follow the jumbled-up lines to find out how big they are!

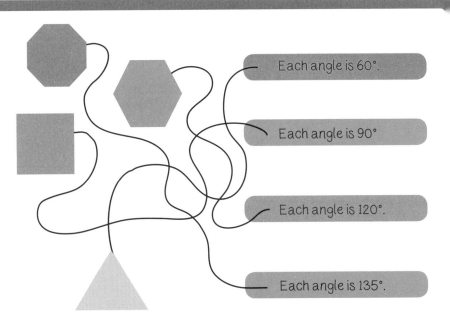

Each angle is 60°.

Each angle is 90°

Each angle is 120°.

Each angle is 135°.

CHECK THE ANSWERS AT THE BACK OF THE BOOK!

Programming codes often use angle measurements for instructions. The code on the right uses 90° rotations to turn the car to the right.

KEY & CODES

○ Roundabout

▢ Parking space

F1 = forward 1 space (the number tells you how many spaces the car should move)

90 = 90° turn

180 = 180° turn

270 = 270° turn

360 = 360° turn

TOP TIP

Angles are measured in a clockwise direction, so:

· A 90° turn is 1 rotation to the right
· A 180° turn is 2 rotations to the right
· A 270° turn is 3 rotations to the right.

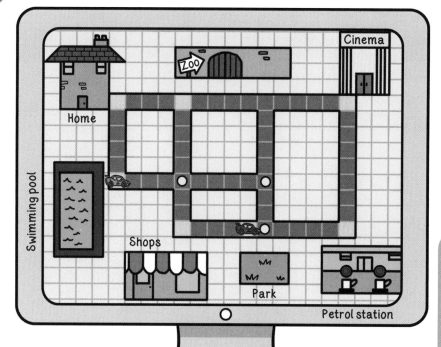

Use the key to follow these programming commands. Start at the swimming pool each time. Where does the blue car end up? Record your answer.

1 F4, 90, F3

2 F4, 270, F5

3 F9, 270, F5, 90, F5

4 Now write some code to program the red car to move from the park to home, with a stop for petrol on the way.

ADA LOVELACE

In 1843 Lovelace, a female mathematician, wrote the first program for a computer, which was referred to as an 'Analytical Engine'.

TRICKY TRIANGLES

A triangle is a 2D (two-dimensional) shape with three sides. The three angles inside a triangle always add up to 180°. There are four main types of triangle.

EQUILATERAL

All three sides are the same length. Each inside angle is the same size.

RIGHT-ANGLED

One angle is 90°.

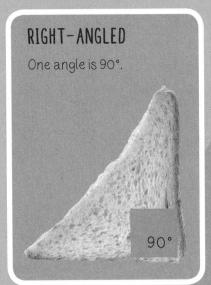

ISOSCELES

Two sides are equal length.

Two of the inside angles are the same size.

SCALENE

All three sides are different lengths. All three inside angles are different sizes.

ACTIVITY

Draw some triangular sails to suit each boat!

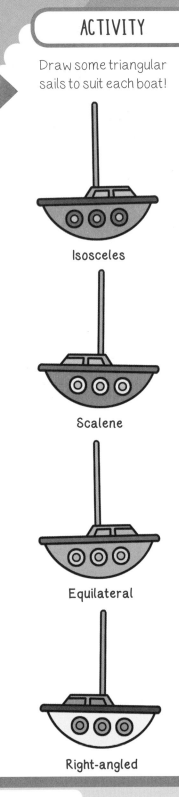

Isosceles

Scalene

Equilateral

Right-angled

CHECK THE ANSWERS AT THE BACK OF THE BOOK!

ACUTE AND OBTUSE

An angle that is less than 90° is called acute.

An angle more than 90° but less than 180° is obtuse.

Acute angle

Obtuse angle

ACTIVITY

How many triangles can you spot in the city?

3D SHAPES

This cereal box is not a flat 2D shape. It has three dimensions — length (or height), width and depth — so it is 3D. It's called a cuboid, which is a 3D shape that has 6 rectangular faces. When those faces are square, like a dice, it is called a cube.

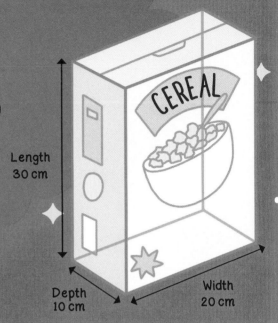

Length
30 cm

Depth
10 cm

Width
20 cm

A 3D shape has volume — the amount of space inside it. Volume can be measured in units of centimetres cubed (cm³) or metres cubed (m³).

To work out the volume of a cube or cuboid, use this equation:

$$\text{VOLUME} = \text{LENGTH} \times \text{WIDTH} \times \text{DEPTH}$$

ACTIVITY

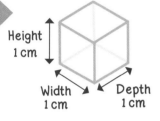

Height
1 cm

Width
1 cm

Depth
1 cm

This dice is 1 cm high, 1 cm wide and 1 cm deep.

Its volume is $1 \times 1 \times 1 = 1 \text{ cm}^3$.

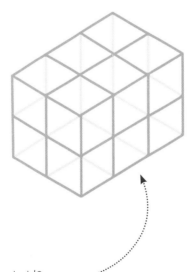

How many dice will fit inside this cuboid?
You can check your answer using the volume equation.

Can you work out the volume of the cereal box at the top of the page? Don't forget the unit of measurement!

If you opened out the cereal box, you would get the 2D shape shown below. This is called a net. A net is a bit like a flattened box that you can fold up to make a 3D shape.

1. Abdi has different shaped boxes to pack up his home-made chocolates one by one. The boxes come to him flat and he has to build them. Help him identify the 3D shape that each of these flat boxes will make when he's finished building them. Circle the correct shape for each flat net.

A
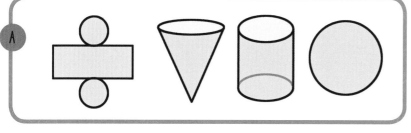

B
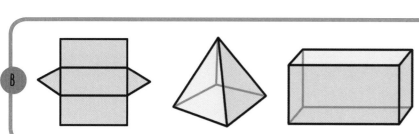

C
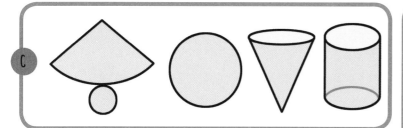

2. Abdi has to order cube-shaped boxes for a special delivery. Which of these nets will NOT make a cube?

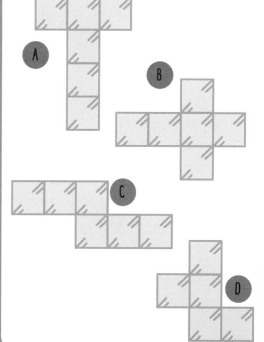

D
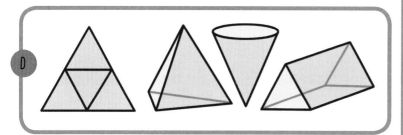

E
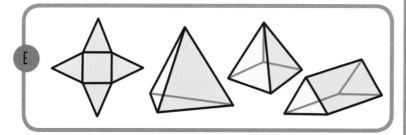

TRANSFORMATION

Objects can keep many of their original properties but can be transformed for new effects. Graphic designers use computer software to transform images all the time. Here are some examples of how shapes can be transformed.

Mirror line

Reflection flips an image over an imaginary 'mirror line'. The reflected image faces the opposite direction of the original image.

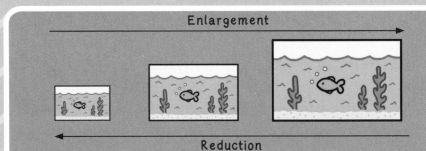

Enlargement

Reduction

Enlargement increases the size of a shape, but keeps its proportions. If you don't maintain the proportions, the object will be distorted. Reduction shrinks the size of an object, while keeping its proportions.

Rotation turns an object around a point of rotation.

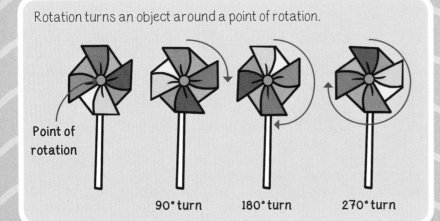

Point of rotation

90° turn   180° turn   270° turn

Translation is when an object stays the same shape, size and angle but moves, or 'slides', in any direction.

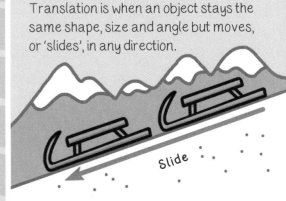

Slide

ACTIVITY

Draw this mug's reflection. Make sure it is the same distance from the mirror line as the original.

Rotate this flag and stick by 180°.

CHECK THE ANSWERS AT THE BACK OF THE BOOK!

Imagine you're a graphic designer. You have altered a photograph to make a new scene for a glossy travel magazine. The magazine editor wants to know all about the transformations so she can get permission from the photographer to use the transformed image. Detail them below.

BEFORE

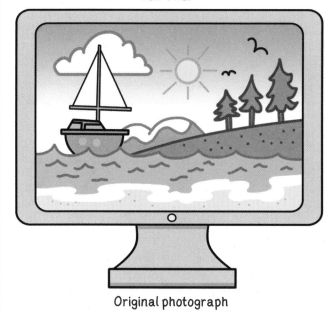

Original photograph

AFTER

Transformed photograph

Translation:

Enlargement:

Reduction:

Reflection:

Rotation:

Slide this dog diagonally upwards to the right.

Enlarge this kite.

GET TESSELLATING!

A tessellation is a repeating pattern of shapes — but not just any shapes! In a tessellation, there cannot be any gaps between the shapes. This means that if we want to tessellate using just one regular polygon, it has to be a triangle, square or hexagon.

ACTIVITY

Finish colouring the square tessellation of this chessboard.

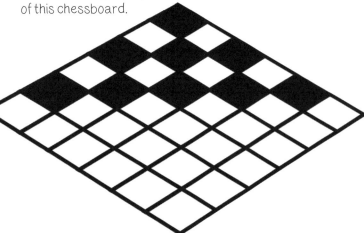

Continue the colour pattern of this tiled floor's triangular tessellation. Does the floor look 3D?

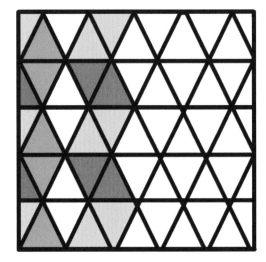

Add some more wax cells to this tessellating hexagonal honeycomb.

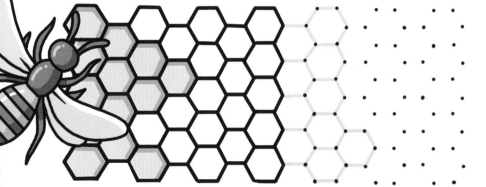

Bees may deliberately build honeycombs of hexagons because these shapes can be packed tightly, creating the most cells with the least amount of wax.

Tessellations can use more than one regular polygon.

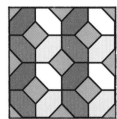
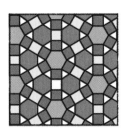
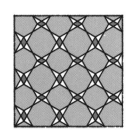

THE BIG MATHS QUIZ

ow it's time to test your skills and see if you really are a maths master!

1 What is the number 3,721 written out in expanded form?

a) 3,000 + 700 + 20 + 2 ☐

b) 3,000 + 700 + 30 + 1 ☐

c) 3,000 + 700 + 20 + 1 ☐

2 What's the name given to numbers that are below zero?

a) Negative ☐

b) Sub zero ☐

c) Negatory ☐

3 On a smartphone, computer or calculator, how is the multiplication symbol often shown?

a) * ☐

b) # ☐

c) $ ☐

4 What does HCF stand for?

a) Highest creeping factor ☐

b) Highest common factor ☐

c) Highest common factory ☐

5 What is the name of the insect that lays its eggs at prime-number intervals?

a) Carrot ☐

b) Canary ☐

c) Cicada ☐

CHECK THE ANSWERS AT THE BACK OF THE BOOK!

6 What is the name of the number that is above the line in a fraction?

a) Denominator ☐

b) Calculator ☐

c) Numerator ☐

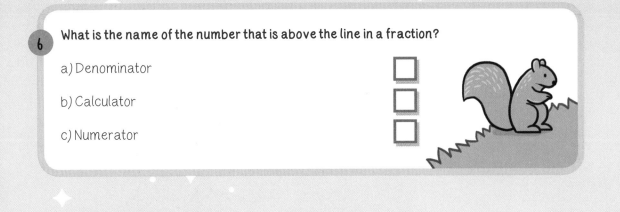

7 How do you write 2,010 in Roman numerals?

a) MPQ ☐

b) MMX ☐

c) MMV ☐

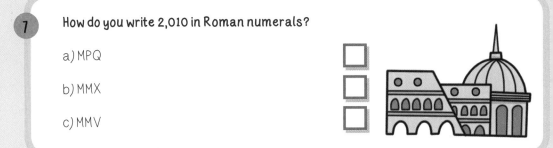

8 What is the name of the number that is used to find out the circumference of a circle?

a) Pi ☐

b) Cake ☐

c) Biscuit ☐

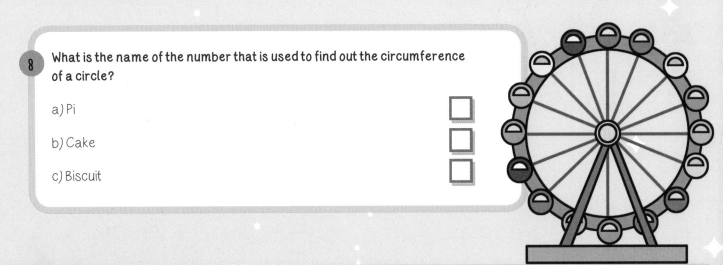

9 Which of these is not a type of triangle?

a) Equilateral ☐

b) Isosceles ☐

c) Extreme ☐

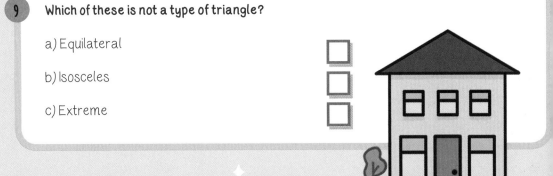

CHECK THE ANSWERS AT THE BACK OF THE BOOK!

ANSWERS

Page 8
COOL COLUMNS
3,725 becomes 3,000 + 700 + 20 + 5
4,159 becomes 4,000 + 100 + 50 + 9
7,022 becomes 7,000 + 0 + 20 + 2

The pattern of increasing numbers is +1, +2, +3, +4, +5, +6, +7, +8, +9, +10

Page 9
SUPER SUMS
Road Sign 1
School to train station = 5 km (7 − 2)
Train station to hospital = 3 km (10 − 7)
School to hospital = 8 km (10 − 2)
Road Sign 2
Park to bus station = 5 km (18 − 13)
Bus station to supermarket = 2 km (20 − 18)
Park to supermarket = 7 km (20 − 13)

Pages 10-11
POPULATION COUNT
Addington
1. 121; 2. 430; 3. 132; 4. 9,443;
5. 1,314; 6. 15,416
Total population: 26,856
Subtractington
1. 18; 2. 38; 3. 509; 4. 396; 5. 5,482;
6. 64,963
Total population: 71,406

44,550 more people live in Subtractington than Addington (71,406 − 26,856).

Pages 12-13
ABOVE AND BELOW ZERO

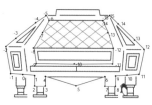

Sunrise: 1 + 8 = 9°C
Midday: 9 − 11 = −2°C
Afternoon: −2 + 5 = 3°C
Nightfall: 3 − 7 = −4°C

Pages 14-15
MULTIPLY AND SUPPLY
Filling the Orders
2 bundles of frisbees: 2 × £8 = £16
2 crates of basketballs: 2 × £9 = £18
2 tubes of tennis balls: 2 × £7 = £14
Increasing the Orders
Holiday camp: £16 × 2 = £32
Sports shop: £18 × 3 = £54
School: £14 × 4 = £56

Pages 16-17
MEET THE MULTIPLES

Amount	Price	Total
7 boxes of hamster food	£10	£70
5 boxes of cat food	£6	£30
6 boxes of dog bones	£4	£24
Grand total:		£124

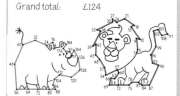

Pages 18-19
SHARE AND DIVIDE
Outdoor Adventure
Fisher's rucksack: 1 water bottle;
2 energy bars; 11 grapes; 3 bananas;
4 worms; 2 hooks
Den-maker's rucksack: 1 water bottle;
2 energy bars; 11 grapes; 3 bananas;
13 sticks; 3 coils of rope

Sharing Marshmallows
3 × 26 = 78 marshmallows in total.
78 ÷ 5 = 15 marshmallows per child, with 3 remaining.
78 ÷ 10 = 7 marshmallows per child, with 8 remaining.

Pages 20-21
FACTOR FACTORY
Factors of 9: 1, 9, 3
Factors of 14: 1, 14, 2, 7
Factors of 21: 1, 21, 3, 7
The HCF of 14 and 21 is 7.

Book Bundles
Mr 12:
4 × 3-pack of books = £40
OR
3 × 4-pack of books = £36
3 × 4-pack of books is cheaper.

Ms 15:
5 × 3-pack of books (5 × £10 = £50)
OR
3 × 5-pack of books (3 × £14 = £42)
3 × 5-pack of books is cheaper.

Mr 20:
5 × 4-pack of books (5 × £12 = £60)
OR
4 × 5-pack of books (4 × £14 = £56)
4 × 5-pack of books is cheaper.

Mrs 21:
7 × 3-pack of books (7 × £10 = £70)
OR
3 × 7-pack of books (3 × £18 = £54)
3 × 7-pack of books is cheaper.

Pages 22-23
NUMBERS IN THEIR PRIME
Colour in all the fish except 61, 103, 23, 7, 67, 43 and 13.

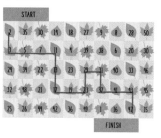

Pages 24-25
CRACK THE CODE
1. 23, 27, 31, 35, 39, **43**
   1, 2, 4, 8, 16, **32**
   20, 15, 11, 8, 6, **5**
   12, 24, 48, 60, **72**
2. The riddle describes the middle padlock. The numbers add up to 7 (2 + 4 + 1).
3. The sum total is 14. The dial cuts through 10 and 4.
4. 21 (Add the two previous numbers 13 + 8)
5. Shortest route = Earth to C to A to B to Earth OR Earth to B to A to C to Earth. Distance = 14 (2 + 4 + 5 + 3 OR 3 + 5 + 4 + 2)

Encryption
Challenge 1 in letters: W, I, L, Y
Challenges 2, 3, 4 and 5 in letters: R, O, C, O.
The thief's name is Wily Roco.

Pages 26-27
FOOD FRACTIONS
Sharing Pizza

There is 1 slice left ($^1/_{12}$).

Squirrels

Pages 28-29
DECIMALS THAT DIVIDE
Crossing the Gorge
2 ½ ➔ 2.5
9 ¼ ➔ 9.25
3.25 ➔ 3 ¼
0.75 ➔ ¾
1 ¾ ➔ 1.75
Shopping List
Total = £7.65
£10.00 − £7.65 = £2.35 change

Pages 30-31
PERCENTAGES

LOADING...25%
LOADING...90%
LOADING...75%

Food Percentages
Water = 50%, $^5/_{10}$ - ½, 0.5
Eggs = 25%, $^{25}/_{100}$ - ¼, 0.25
Cake = 75%, $^{75}/_{100}$ - ¾, 0.75

Pages 32-33
WHAT'S THE TIME?

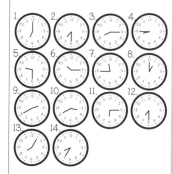

Pages 34-35
ROMAN NUMERALS

Roman Years
1. MMX = 2010
2. MMXXIX = 2029
3. MMLXIV = 2064

Number Search

1. DCCLIII
2. LXIV
3. LXXX
4. CCCXCV

Pages 36-37
MEASURING MAYHEM
Building Parts
Correct door: 85 cm by 203 cm
Correct window: 1.25 m by 1.7 m
Correct beam: 5,500 mm
Bricks: 42 (4.2 m = 420 cm = 4,200 mm; 4,200 ÷ 100 = 42)

Bags of Sand
Bag A 1,000 g = 1 kg
Bag B 10,000 g = 10 kg
Bag C 100 g = 0.1 kg
Unloading order: B, A, C.

Pages 38-39
SPORTS DAY
Hurdles

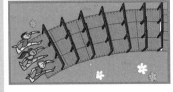

Javelin
Jade: 16 metres; Maria: 8 metres;
Juan: 32 metres; Chris: 18 metres;
Simon: 29 metres

Sprint
Name	Time (seconds)	Position
Lucy	14.32	6th
Amir	14.23	4th
Alexander	14.01	1st
Rosa	14.10	2nd
Tariq	14.31	5th
Imani	14.13	3rd

Half Marathon
Name	Time	Time in hours, minutes, seconds
Salma	79 minutes 22 seconds	1 h 19 m 22 s
Zara	125 minutes 51 seconds	2 h 5 m 51 s
Ben	120 minutes 30 seconds	2 h 0 m 30 s

Gold = Salma
Silver = Ben
Bronze = Zara

Pages 40-41
WILDLIFE WATCH
Sloths, Snakes and Butterflies
Snakes in the eastern area: 23
Total creatures in the northern area: 82
Sloths in the whole reserve: 6
Most common animal: butterfly

Monkeys
Passion fruits eaten by males: 8
Nuts eaten by females: 6
Passion fruits eaten in total: 12
Passion fruits and nuts eaten by females: 10
Leaf symbols: draw 3 for the female monkeys and 2 ½ for the male monkeys

Birds
Green parrots =
Blue parrots =
Green parrots on Wednesday: 11
Most blue parrots: Friday
Parrots in total on the weekend: 18
Green parrots altogether = 71

River Animals

Parrot Colours

Pages 42-43
FIRST-RATE RATIOS
Animal Ratios
1. Draw 6 lions; 2. Draw 4 beetles;
3. Draw 3 sharks

Ingredient Ratios
Coconut milk : water = 4:1
Chilli powder : coriander powder = 3:4
Green beans : red pepper = 2:3
Cloves of garlic : whole onions = 3:1

Pages 44-45
TREASURE HUNT
1. (8, 8) = volcano
   (10, 5) = elephant statue
   (11, 10) = anchor
   (6, 12) = crab
2. The treasure is in the cave (3, 7).
3. Palm tree = (5, 4)
   Sea rock = (12, 1)
   Swamp = (4, 9)
   Lighthouse = (2, 13)
4. Beach = 3 km long
   Island width = 13 km
   Path = 3.5 km
   Tower to anchor = 4 km

Pages 46-47
PERFECT POLYGONS
Hidden Animal

	Sides	Vertices
Triangle	3	3
Square	4	4
Rectangle	4	4
Pentagon	5	5
Hexagon	6	6

The square and rectangle are both quadrilaterals.

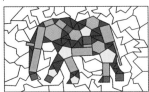

Understanding Area
Missing field lengths: cow field 70 m; sheep field 60 m.
Cow field area: 70 × 90 = 6,300 m²
Chicken field area: 30 × 90 = 2,700 m²
Sheep field area: 60 × 100 = 6,000 m²
Total area of the farm: 6,300 + 2,700 + 6,000 = 15,000 m² OR 150 × 100 = 15,000 m²
Perimeter: 150 + 100 + 150 + 100 = 500 m OR 100 + 150 + 70 + 30 + 90 + 60 = 500 m

Pages 48-49
SUPER SYMMETRY
Lines of symmetry

Symmetrical Birds

Pages 50-51
PIECES OF PI
Zoo
Circumference of penguin pool:
9 x 3.14 = 28.26 m
Circumference of crocodile pool:
12 x 3.14 = 37.68 m

Planets
ZOG circumference: 2,826 km.
Assigned rocket: A
ZAG circumference: 6,280 km.
Assigned rocket: C
ZIG circumference: 7,850 km.
Assigned rocket: B

Pages 52-53
AWESOME ANGLES
Regular Polygons
Triangle: each angle is 60°
Square: each angle is 90°
Hexagon: each angle is 120°
Octagon: each angle is 135°

Car Coding
1. Shops
2. Zoo
3. Cinema
4. F6, 270, F8, 270, F14

Pages 54-55:
TRICKY TRIANGLES
Sailing Boats

Isosceles   Scalene   Equilateral   Right-angled

Triangles in the City: 26 in total

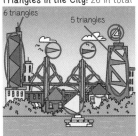

6 triangles   5 triangles

Pages 56-57
3D SHAPES
Volume
12 dice would fit in the cuboid. Volume is 12 cm³ (3 × 2 × 2).
The volume of the cereal box is 6,000 cm³ (30 × 20 × 10).

Chocolate Boxes
1.  A. Cylinder
 B. Triangular prism
 C. Cone
D. Triangular pyramid
E. Square-bottomed pyramid
2. Net D would not make a cube.

Pages 58-59
TRANSFORMATION
Transforming Objects

Altered Image
Translation: tree
Reduction: cloud
Rotation: bird
Enlargement: sun
Reflection: boat

Page 60
GET TESSELLATING!

Pages 61-62
THE BIG MATHS QUIZ
1. c   2. a   3. a   4. b   5. c
6. c   7. b   8. a   9. c